WHSmith

Progress Tests

Spelling

Louis Fidge

Hachette UK's policy is to use papers that are natural, renewable and recyclable products and made from wood grown in sustainable forests. The logging and manufacturing processes are expected to conform to the environmental regulations of the country of origin.

Orders: please contact Bookpoint Ltd, 130 Milton Park, Abingdon, Oxon OX14 4SB. Telephone: (44) 01235 827720. Fax: (44) 01235 400454. Lines are open 9.00a.m.–5.00p.m., Monday to Saturday, with a 24-hour message answering service. Visit our website at www.hoddereducation.co.uk.

First published in 2007 exclusively for WHSmith by
Hodder Education
An Hachette UK Company
338 Euston Road
London NW1 3BH

This second edition first published in 2013 exclusively for WHSmith by Hodder Education.

Impression number 10 9 8 7 6 5 4 3 2 1
Year 2018 2017 2016 2015 2014 2013

Cover illustration by Oxford Designers and Illustrators Ltd
All other illustrations by Fakenham Prepress Solutions, Fakenham, Norfolk NR21 8NN
Typeset in 16pt Folio by Fakenham Prepress Solutions, Fakenham, Norfolk NR21 8NN
Printed in Great Britain by Hobbs the Printers Ltd, Totton, Hampshire SO40 3WX

A catalogue record for this title is available from the British Library.

ISBN: 978 1444 188 219

Age 6–7
Year 2
Key Stage 1

Introduction

Progress Tests: Spelling

- Spelling is a key feature of the National Curriculum and the National Literacy Framework.
- Children need to be able to spell in order to read and write fluently and confidently.
- Good spelling is essential in all areas of the curriculum.
- Learning to spell requires constant practice and reinforcement.
- This series of 'teach and test' books will help build your child's confidence and ability in spelling.

Features of the books

- Each test:
  - has a clear spelling focus
  - introduces ten words which contain the same spelling focus
  - has a range of activities which help your child to learn to spell the words
  - finishes with a spelling test, using the ten Test words.
- Answers to the activities may be found on pages 35–40.
- A record sheet is provided on page 3 on which your child can keep a record of all spelling test scores.

How to do the tests

- Do one test each week.
- Agree on a set time with your child, and keep it the same each week if possible.
- Ensure your child can read the Test words at the top of the page and knows their meanings.
- Encourage your child to do the activities to help learn the words.
- On completion of the activities, get your child to do the spelling test.

How to do the spelling tests

- Turn to pages 41–48 and find the appropriate answer sheet to complete.
- Ask your child to look back at the Test words and study these again for a short while.
- Then either:
  - copy out the words and read them slowly to your child (or get another adult or child to read them)

  or:
  - ask your child to write the words from memory (without copying them!)
- When the spelling test has been completed, ask your child to mark it by referring back to the Test words and checking their spellings.
- After each spelling test, ask your child to colour in the score on the record sheet on the inside back cover.

Test 1: Spelling with phonemes

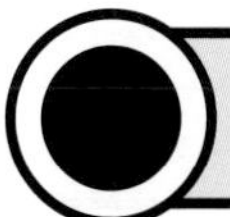

Test words

bat	bed	zip	fox	bun
pan	leg	six	mop	hut

When you spell a simple word you:

- say each phoneme (sound) b + a + t
- put the phonemes (sounds) together b a t
- read the word bat

1. Read the ten Test words.
2. Do these phoneme sums. Write the words you make.

   a) z + i + p = ______ **b)** m + o + p = ______

   c) b + a + t = ______ **d)** h + u + t = ______

   e) l + e + g = ______ **f)** s + i + x = ______

   g) f + o + x = ______ **h)** p + a + n = ______

   i) b + u + n = ______ **j)** b + e + d = ______

3. Use the correct word in each sentence.

   a) You hit a ball with a ________.

   b) A ________ is like a cake.

   c) You sleep in a ________.

   d) You cook things in a ________.

   e) I can stand on one ________.

4. Now do **Spelling Test 1** on page 41.

Test 2: Rhyming words

Test words

cat	hen	tin	log	mug
jug	dog	pen	bin	hat

1. Read the ten Test words.
2. Do these phoneme sums. Write the words you make.

a) c + a + t = _________ **b)** h + a + t = _________

c) h + e + n = _________ **d)** p + e + n = _________

e) t + i + n = _________ **f)** b + i + n = _________

g) l + o + g = _________ **h)** d + o + g = _________

i) m + u + g = _________ **j)** j + u + g = _________

3. Change some letters.Write each new word you make.

a) Change the **c** in **c**at to **h**.
____

b) Change the **h** in **h**en to **p**.
____

c) Change the **t** in **t**in to **b**.
____

d) Change the **l** in **l**og to **d**.
____

4. Use the correct word in each sentence.

a) A _________ says 'miaow'.

b) You wear a _________ on your head.

c) You drink from a _________.

d) You put water in a _________.

5. Now do **Spelling Test 2** on page 41.

Test 3: Some phonemes sound the same (1)

Test words

sleep	street	feel	three	queen
speak	clean	seat	teach	beast

1. Read the ten Test words. (Note that in these words the phonemes **ee** and **ea** sound the same.)

2. Complete each word with **ee** or **ea**. Write the word you make.

   a) street *street* **b)** cl____n ____________

   c) f____l ____________ **d)** t____ch ____________

   e) sp____k ____________ **f)** thr____ ____________

   g) b____st ____________ **h)** sl____p ____________

   i) qu____n ____________ **j)** s____t ____________

3. Use the correct word in each sentence.

   a) You ____________ in a bed.

   b) The king and ____________ live in a castle.

   c) There were ____________ Billy Goats Gruff.

   d) I live on a busy ____________.

   e) The old man sat down on a ____________ to rest.

   f) The troll was an ugly ____________.

   g) You wash your hands to make them ____________.

   h) In a library you must ____________ quietly.

   i) On my birthday I always ____________ happy.

4. Now do **Spelling Test 3** on page 41.

Test 4: Some phonemes sound the same (2)

Test words

snail	paint	afraid	rain	aim
tray	clay	spray	holiday	yesterday

1. Read the ten Test Words. (Note that in these words the phonemes **ai** and **ay** sound the same.)

2. Which **ay** word begins with:

   a) **c**? ____________ **b)** **h**? ____________ **c)** **t**? ____________

   d) **y**? ____________ **e)** **s**? ____________

3. Which **ai** word ends with:

   a) **t**?____________ **b)** **m**? ____________ **c)** **l**? ____________

   d) **n**? ____________ **e)** **d**? ____________

4. Use the correct word in each sentence.

   a) The baker carried some cakes on a ____________.

   b) In the summer we went to Spain on ____________.

   c) If you play in the ____________ you will get wet.

   d) I love to ____________ pictures.

   e) ____________ I fell off my bike.

   f) A ____________ lives in a shell.

   g) I am not ____________ of spiders.

   h) I like to ____________ my sister with the hosepipe!

   i) You can make things out of ____________.

5. Now do **Spelling Test 4** on page 41.

Test 5: Some phonemes sound the same (3)

Test words

sky fly cry reply why

high sigh right night light

1. Read the ten Test words. (Note that in these words the phonemes **y** and **igh** sound the same.)
2. Write the **y** words in alphabetical order.

   __________ __________ __________ __________ __________
3. Write the two words that end with **igh**.

   __________ __________
4. Write the words that have **igh** in the middle.

   __________ __________ __________
5. Use the correct word in each sentence.

   a) A bird can __________.

   b) The stars come out at __________.

   c) I got my spellings all __________.

   d) When it gets dark I turn on the __________.

   e) The __________ is blue.

   f) If I hurt myself I __________.

   g) The opposite of low is __________.

   h) I had to __________ to the invitation I received.

   i) I don’t know __________ some trees lose their leaves.
6. Now do **Spelling Test 5** on page 42.

Test 6: y

Test words

m__ cr__ dr__ fr__ tr__

sk__ sh__ wh__ fl__ repl__

1. Add **y** to the end of each word in the box above.
   Read the ten Test words you make.

2. Write:

   a) the shortest word ____________

   b) the longest word ____________

3. Write the words that have **r** as their second letter.

   ____________ ____________ ____________ ____________

4. Write the words that begin with **s**.

   ____________ ____________

5. Write the two words that are left.

   ____________ ____________

6. Now do **Spelling Test 6** on page 42.

Test 7: **igh**

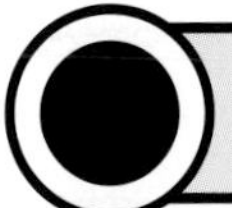

Test words

h___	s____	th____	n____t	l____t
f___t	m___t	r____t	s____t	t____t

1. Add the missing **igh** to each word in the box above.
   Read the ten Test words you make.

2. Change some letters. Read the new words you make.

   a) Change the **h** in **h**igh to **s** *sigh*

   b) Change the **s** in **s**igh to **th** ____________

   c) Change the **th** in **th**igh to **h** ____________

   d) Change the **n** in **n**ight to **l** ____________

   e) Change the **l** in **l**ight to **f** ____________

   f) Change the **f** in **f**ight to **m** ____________

   g) Change the **m** in **m**ight to **r** ____________

   h) Change the **r** in **r**ight to **s** ____________

   i) Change the **s** in **s**ight to **t** ____________

   j) Change the **t** in **t**ight to **n** ____________

3. Now do **Spelling Test 7** on page 42.

Test 8: **i–e** (magic **e**)

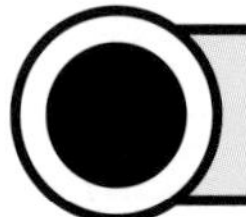

Test words

lik__ div__ fin__ rid__ til__

smil__ wid__ fiv__ shin__ bik__

1. Add the magic **e** to the end of each word in the box above. Read the ten Test words you make.

2. Write the word that rhymes with:

a) like ____________ **b)** dive ____________

c) fine ____________ **d)** ride ____________

e) tile ____________

3. Read the sentences. Underline the 'magic e' words in them.

a) I like to ride my bike.

b) If it is fine the sun will shine.

c) Look at my wide smile!

d) Five tiles fell off the roof of my house.

e) I can dive in the water and swim.

4. Now do **Spelling Test 8** on page 42.

Test 9: **oa**

Test words

b___t   c___t   g___t   r___d   t___d

c___st   t___st   s___k   cr___k   cl___k

1. Add the missing **oa** to each word in the box above.
   Read the ten Test words you make.
2. Complete the chart.

oak words	**oat** words	**oast** words	**oad** words

3. Choose the correct word for each sentence.

   a) You row a ________ (boat, coat, goat).

   b) A ________ (road, toad) is like a frog.

   c) You can eat ________ (coast, toast).

   d) A frog can ________ (croak, cloak).

4. Now do **Spelling Test 9** on page 43.

Test 10: **ow**

Test words

l___	r___	m___	cr___	sn___
sl___	bl___	gr___	wind___	yell___

1. Add **ow** to the end of each word in the box above.
   Read the ten Test words you make.

2. Which words have:

   a) three letters? ________ ________ ________

   b) four letters? ______ ______ ______ ______ ______

   c) six letters? ____________ ____________

3. Write the opposite of:

   a) high ________ **b)** fast ________ **c)** suck ________

4. Choose the word that means:

   a) something cold ____________

   b) the colour of the sun ____________

   c) something you do to grass ____________

   d) something you do in a boat ____________

   e) to get bigger ____________

   f) a black bird ____________

   g) something you look out of ____________

5. Now do **Spelling Test 10** on page 43.

Test 11: **o–e** (magic **e**)

Test words

jok__	hop__	bon__	rob__	mol__
hol__	lob__	slop__	con__	smok__

1. Add the magic **e** to the end of each word in the box above. Read the ten Test words you make.

2. Write the word that rhymes with:

   a) joke ____________ **b)** hope ____________

   c) bone ____________ **d)** robe ____________

   e) mole ____________

3. Read the sentences. Underline the 'magic e' words in them.

   a) The mole is in a hole.

   b) I hope I don't slip down the slope.

   c) You wear a robe.

   d) Do you want a bone or an ice-cream cone?

   e) You tell a joke.

   f) My ear has got a lobe.

   g) Lots of smoke came from the fire.

4. Now do **Spelling Test 11** on page 43.

Test 12: **ew**

Test words

n___	f___	d___	ch___	dr___
gr___	thr___	st___	bl___	fl___

1. Add **ew** to the end of each word in the box above.
   Read the ten Test words you make.

2. Choose the correct word for each sentence.

   a) The grass was wet with _______ (few, dew).

   b) The girl _______ (drew, grew) a lovely picture.

   c) You must always _______ (blew, chew) your food.

   d) I liked my _______ (new, flew) trainers.

   e) I only have a _______ (few, flew) sweets left.

   f) The wind _______ (stew, blew) my hat off.

   g) The birds _______ (few, flew) in the sky.

   h) The boy _______ (new, threw) the ball.

   i) You can eat _______ (blew, stew).

   j) The man _______ (grew, threw) flowers in his garden.

3. Now do **Spelling Test 12** on page 43.

Test 13: **oo**

Test words

b___t r___t f___d m___d c___l

st___l h___p sw___p m___n sp___n

1. Add the missing **oo** to each word in the box above. Read the ten Test words you make.

2. Change some letters. Read the new words you make.

   a) Change the **b** in **b**oot to **r** *root*

   b) Change the **f** in **f**ood to **m** __________

   c) Change the **c** in **c**ool to **st** __________

   d) Change the **h** in **h**oop to **sw** __________

   e) Change the **m** in **m**oon to **sp** __________

   f) Change the **r** in **r**oot to **b** __________

   g) Change the **m** in **m**ood to **f** __________

   h) Change the **st** in **st**ool to **c** __________

   i) Change the **sw** in **sw**oop to **h** __________

   j) Change the **sp** in **sp**oon to **m** __________

3. Now do **Spelling Test 13** on page 44.

Test 14: **u–e** (magic **e**)

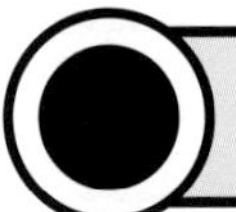

Test words

cub__	tub__	rud__	tun__	flut__
cut__	mul__	rul__	us__	duk__

1. Add the magic **e** to the end of each word in the box above. Read the ten Test words you make.

2. Underline the magic **e** word. Write the magic **e** word.

a) q w r t u b e o p m — *tube*

b) t u n e x c b g d s — __________

c) p l k h t z d u k e — __________

d) k d f r u l e x c v — __________

e) n b c u t e g j h y — __________

f) m u l e w q s a b m — __________

g) k t r w s r u d e z — __________

h) n c u b e p t r w x — __________

i) k l p y f l u t e c — __________

j) w q f s z d v u s e — __________

3. Now do **Spelling Test 14** on page 44.

Test 15: Magic **e** words

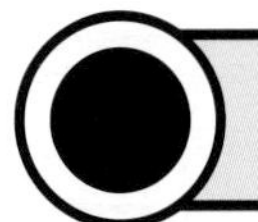

Test words

hate	mane	cape	shine	pipe
robe	hope	note	tube	cute

1. Read the ten Test words.

2. Write the Test words again but take the magic **e** off the end of each word. Read the words you make.

   hat ________ ________ ________ ________

   ________ ________ ________ ________ ________

3. Use the correct word in each sentence.

   a) A male lion has a __________.

   b) I __________ it does not rain tomorrow.

   c) I squeezed some toothpaste from the __________.

   d) If it is fine the sun will __________.

   e) I wrote a __________ to my friend.

   f) Water comes through a __________ under the ground.

   g) The little baby looked very __________ in her new clothes.

   h) I don't like cabbage, in fact, I __________ it!

   i) The king was wearing a __________ made of silk.

   j) Batman wears a __________ on his back.

4. Now do **Spelling Test 15** on page 44.

Test 16: ar

Test words

c___	st___	b___k	d___k	___m
f___m	c___d	h___d	st___t	c___t

1. Add the missing **ar** to each word in the box above.
   Read the ten Test words you make.

2. Write the opposite of:

   a) light _______

   b) soft _______

   c) stop _______

3. Choose the correct word.

   a) A dog can do this. ___________

   b) You ride in this. ___________

   c) Your hand is at the end of this. ___________

   d) You see this in the sky. ___________

   e) You see cows here. ___________

   f) A horse can pull this. ___________

   g) You get this on your birthday. ___________

4. Now do **Spelling Test 16** on page 44.

Test 17: **a**

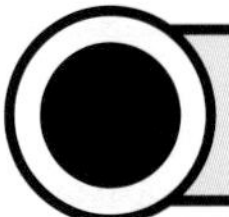

Test words

f__st   l__st   pl__ster   gl__ss   gr__ss

b__th   p__th   __sk   m__sk   b__sket

1. Add the missing **a** to each word in the box above.
   Read the ten Test words you make.

2. Choose the word that means:

   a) the opposite of slow ____________

   b) the opposite of first ____________

   c) something that is green ____________

   d) something you put shopping in ____________

   e) something you drink out of ____________

   f) something you can wash in ____________

   g) something you walk on ____________

   h) something you put on a cut ____________

   i) something you wear on your face ____________

   j) what you do when you want to know an answer ____________

3. Now do **Spelling Test 17** on page 45.

Test 18: **ou**

Test words

m___se h___se m___th s___th l___d

cl___d s___nd f___nd ___t sh___t

1. Add the missing **ou** to each word in the box above.
   Read the ten Test words you make.

2. Write the words that contain:

out	**outh**	**ouse**	**oud**	**ound**

3. Read the sentences. Underline the **ou** words in them.

   a) I found a mouse in the house.

   b) I opened my mouth to shout out loud.

   c) There was a big black cloud in the south.

   d) When I am quiet I don't make a sound.

4. Now do **Spelling Test 18** on page 45.

Test 19: **ow**

Test words

c___ h___ ___l h___l gr___l

fl___er sh___er cl___n d___n cr___d

1. Add the missing **ow** to each word in the box above. Read the ten Test words you make.

2. Which words have:

   a) three letters? ___________ ___________ ___________

   b) four letters? ___________ ___________

   c) five letters? ___________ ___________ ___________

   d) six letters? ___________ ___________

3. Choose the correct word for each sentence.

   a) A _________ (owl, cow) gives us milk.

   b) A lion can _________ (howl, growl).

   c) There are a lot of people in a _________ (crowd, how).

   d) A _________ (flower, shower) grows in the ground.

   e) A _________ (down, clown) makes you smile.

4. Now do **Spelling Test 19** on page 45.

Test 20: **oy**

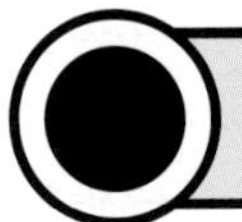

Test words

t___ b___ j___ c___ enj___

empl___ ann___ destr___ ___ster r___al

1. Add the missing **oy** to each word in the box above.
   Read the ten Test words you make.

2. Which words:

   a) begin with **oy**? _______

   b) end with **oy**? _______ _______ _______ _______

   _______ _______ _______ _______

   c) have **oy** in the middle? _______

3. Write the sets of words in alphabetical order.

   a) toy boy joy coy enjoy

   _______ _______ _______ _______ _______

   b) employ annoy destroy oyster royal

   _______ _______ _______ _______ _______

4. Now do **Spelling Test 20** on page 45.

Test 21: **oi**

Test words

___l   b___l   c___l   f___l   sp___l

c___n   j___n   p___nt   n___se   v___ce

1. Add the missing **oi** to each word in the box above.
   Read the ten Test words you make.

2. Add **b**, **c**, **f** and **sp** to the beginning of **oil** to make four new words.

   ________ ________ ________ ________

3. Write the **oi** word that means:

   a) to fix together ________

   b) money ________

   c) a sharp end ________

   d) the thing you talk with ________

   e) a sound ________

4. Now do **Spelling Test 21** on page 46.

Test 22: **u** and **oo**

Test words

p___t	b___sh	p___sh	f___ll	p___ll
b___k	c___k	l___k	g___d	w___d

1. Add the missing **u** to the *first five* words in the box above.
   Add the missing **oo** to the *second five* words in the box above.
   Read the ten Test words you make.

2. Which word contains three letters? ______

3. Write the words that rhyme with:

   a) bush ______ **b)** full ______

   c) good ______ **d)** book ______ ______

4. Read the sentences. Underline the **u** and **oo** words in them.

   a) Let me look at that cook book.

   b) It is not nice to pull or push someone in a bush.

   c) You can't put more water in a glass that is full.

   d) It is good to walk in the wood.

5. Now do **Spelling Test 22** on page 46.

Test 23: **ea**

Test words

h___d d___d br___d tr___d spr___d

h___vy r___dy st___dy f___ther w___ther

1. Add the missing **ea** to each word in the box above.
   Read the ten Test words you make.

2. Which word ends with **vy**? __________

3. Change some letters. Read the new words you make.

   a) Change the **h** in **h**ead to **d** *dead*

   b) Change the **d** in **d**ead to **br** __________

   c) Change the **br** in **br**ead to **h** __________

   d) Change the **tr** in **tr**ead to **spr** __________

   e) Change the **spr** in **spr**ead to **tr** __________

   f) Change the **r** in **r**eady to **st** __________

   g) Change the **st** in **st**eady to **r** __________

   h) Change the **f** in **f**eather to **w** __________

   i) Change the **w** in **w**eather to **f** __________

4. Now do **Spelling Test 23** on page 46.

Test 24: Same spelling pattern, different sound (1)

Test words

foot	cook	wood	hook	good
boot	food	pool	broom	roof

1. Read the ten Test words.
2. Make these words. The words all have a long **oo** sound.

   a) f*oo*d b____t p____l r____f br____m

   Now make these words. The words all have a short **oo** sound:

   b) c____ k w____d h____k g____d f____t
3. Use the correct word in each sentence.

   a) A ________ is like a shoe.

   b) You ________ things in a saucepan.

   c) I have five toes on each ________.

   d) In the ________ we saw a deer.

   e) You sweep the floor with a ________.

   f) The opposite of bad is ________.

   g) We eat ________.

   h) The ________ of my house is made of tiles.

   i) We went for a swim in the ________.

   j) You catch fish with a ________.
4. Now do **Spelling Test 24** on page 46.

Test 25: Same spelling pattern, different sound (2)

Test words

seat weak team beach season

sweat deaf meadow leather jealous

1. Read the ten Test words.
2. Make these words. The words all have a long **ea** sound:

   a) beach t____m s____t w____k s____son

   Now make these words. The words all have a short **ea** sound:

   b) d____f sw____t l____ther j____lous m____dow
3. Use the correct word in each sentence.

   a) If you get too hot you __________.

   b) Our school __________ won the swimming cup.

   c) If you can't hear you are __________.

   d) Spring is the name of a __________.

   e) You sit on a __________.

   f) The __________ was made of sand and pebbles.

   g) Some shoes are made of __________.

   h) After my illness I felt very __________.

   i) There were two ponies in the __________.

   j) The boy was __________ of his sister's new bike.
4. Now do **Spelling Test 25** on page 47.

Test 26: **wh**

Test words

___y	___at	___en	___ere	___ich
___eel	___isk	___eat	___ale	___ite

1. Add the missing **wh** to the beginning of each word in the box above. Read the ten Test words you make.

2. Which word is:

   a) a colour? ____________

   b) something you find in a kitchen? ____________

   c) something bread is made of? ____________

   d) an animal that lives in the sea? ____________

   e) something that is round? ____________

3. Underline the **wh** words. Answer the questions.

   a) What is your name? ________________

   b) Where do you live? ________________

   c) Why do you go to school? ________________

   d) When do you go to bed? ________________

   e) Which fruit do you like best? ________________

4. Now do **Spelling Test 26** on page 47.

Test 27: Compound words

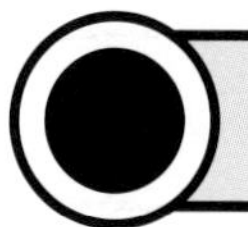

Test words

rainbow butterfly windmill toothbrush bookcase

handbag sunshine moonlight playground seaside

1. Read the ten Test words.
2. Do these word sums.

a) tooth + brush = *toothbrush* **b)** play+ ground = ________

c) hand + bag = ________ **d)** rain + bow = ________

e) moon + light = ________ **f)** sea + side = ________

g) butter + fly = ________ **h)** book + case = ________

i) wind + mill = ________ **j)** sun + shine = ________

3. Use the correct word in each sentence.

a) After the storm there was a ________ in the sky.

b) We played on the beach at the ________.

c) You clean your teeth with a ________.

d) At playtime we went into the ________.

e) The lady picked up her ________.

f) The beautiful ________ landed on the flower.

g) I put the book on the shelf of the ________.

h) It is hot in the ________.

i) The sails of the ________ turned round.

j) We could see clearly at night because of the ________.

4. Now do **Spelling Test 27** on page 47.

Test 28: Key words (1)

Test words

April   August   December   February   January

July   March   November   October   September

1. Read the ten Test words.

2. Write the months of the year in the correct order.

a)	______	**b)**	______	**c)**	______
d)	______	**e)**	*May*	**f)**	*June*
g)	______	**h)**	______	**i)**	______
j)	______	**k)**	______	**l)**	______

3. Which is the:

   a) first month of the year? ______

   b) last month of the year? ______

   c) second month? ______

   d) tenth month? ______

   e) eleventh month? ______

4. Which two months begin with A? ______ ______

5. Now do **Spelling Test 28** on page 47.

Test 29: Key words (2)

Test words

eye	hair	nose	ear	cheek
chin	lip	neck	forehead	face

1. Read the ten Test words.
2. Write the words that contain:
   a) three letters _______ _______ _______
   b) four letters _______ _______ _______ _______ _______
   c) five letters _______
   d) eight letters _______
3. Which word:
   a) ends with **p**? __________ **b)** ends with **ck**? __________
   c) ends with **air**? __________ **d)** ends with **ace**? __________
   e) ends with **ose**? __________ **f)** ends with **head**? __________
   g) begins and ends with the same letter? _____
4. Which two words begin with ch? ________ ________
5. Complete this sentence: You hear with your ________.
6. Now do **Spelling Test 29** on page 48.

Test 30: Key words (3)

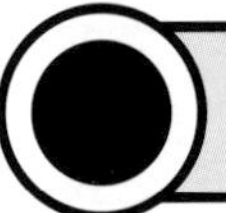

Test words

bath	bed	mat	chair	cooker
door	clock	sink	window	table

1. Read the ten Test words.
2. Fill in the missing vowels in these words.

   a) m__t   **b)** t__bl__   **c)** d__r

   d) b__th   **e)** s__nk   **f)** cl__ck

   g) b__d   **h)** w__nd__w   **i)** ch__ r

   j) c__k__r
3. Write the answers.

   a) You get clean in this. ____________

   b) You look out of this. ____________

   c) You sleep in this. ____________

   d) You wash dishes in this. ____________

   e) This tells you the time. ____________

   f) You sit on this. ____________

   g) You sit at this to eat. ____________

   h) You open this to go into a room. ____________

   i) You cook on this. ____________

   j) This rhymes with cat. ____________
4. Now do **Spelling Test 30** on page 48.

Test 31: Key words (4)

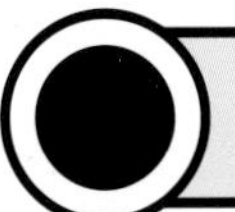

Test words

wind	**rain**	**snow**	**fog**	**frost**
mist	**ice**	**sleet**	**sunshine**	**gale**

1. Read the ten Test words. (They are all to do with the weather.)
2. Write the words with three letters.

   ________ ________

3. Write the words with four letters.

   ________ ________ ________ ________ ________

4. Write the words with five letters.

   ________________ ________________

5. Write the longest weather word. ________________
6. Write the word that rhymes with:

   a) pain ____________ **b)** lost ____________

   c) whale ____________ **d)** list ____________

   e) sheet ____________ **f)** cog ____________

   g) slow ____________ **h)** mice ____________

   i) mine ____________

7. Now do **Spelling Test 31** on page 48.

Answers

Test 1

2 a zip b mop
c bat d hut
e leg f six
g fox h pan
i bun j bed

3 a bat b bun
c bed d pan
e leg

Test 2

2 a cat b hat
c hen d pen
e tin f bin
g log h dog
i mug j jug

3 a hat b pen
c bin d dog

4 a cat b hat
c mug d jug

Test 3

2 a street b clean
c feel d teach
e speak f three
g beast h sleep
i queen j seat

3 a sleep b queen
c three d street
e seat f beast
g clean h speak
i feel

Test 4

2 a clay b holiday
c tray d yesterday
e spray

3 a paint b aim
c snail d rain
e afraid

4 a tray b holiday
c rain d paint
e Yesterday f snail
g afraid h spray
i clay

Test 5

2 cry fly reply sky why

3 high sigh

4 right night light

5 a fly b night c right
d light e sky f cry
g high h reply i why

Test 6

1 my cry dry fry try
sky shy why fly reply

2 a my b reply

3 cry dry fry try

4 sky shy

5 why fly

Test 7

1 high sigh thigh night light
fight might right sight tight

2 a sigh b thigh c high d light
e fight f might g right h sight
i tight j night

Test 8

1 like dive fine ride tile
smile wide five shine bike

2 a bike
b five
c shine
d wide
e smile

3 a I like to ride my bike.
b If it is fine the sun will shine.
c Look at my wide smile!
d Five tiles fell off the roof of my house.
e I can dive in the water and swim.

Test 9

1 boat coat goat road toad
coast toast soak croak
cloak

2

oak words	**oat** words
soak	boat
croak	coat
cloak	goat
oast words	**oad** words
coast	road
toast	toad

3 a boat b toad c toast d croak

Test 10

1 low row mow crow snow
slow blow grow window
yellow

2 a low row mow
b crow snow slow blow grow
c window yellow

3 a low
b slow
c blow

4 a snow b yellow c mow
d row e grow f crow
g window

Test 11

1 joke hope bone robe mole
hole lobe slope cone smoke

2 a smoke b slope c cone
d lobe e hole

3 a The mole is in a hole.
b I hope I don't slip down the slope.
c You wear a robe.
d Do you want a bone or an ice-cream cone?
e You tell a joke.
f My ear has got a lobe.
g Lots of smoke came from the fire.

Test 12

1 new few dew chew drew
grew threw stew blew flew

2 a dew b drew
c chew d new
e few f blew
g flew h threw
i stew j grew

Test 13

1 boot root food mood cool
stool hoop swoop moon
spoon

2 a root b mood c stool
d swoop e spoon f boot
g food h cool i hoop
j moon

Test 14

1 cube tube rude tune flute
cute mule rule use duke

2 a q w r t u b e o p m tube
b t u n e x c b g d s tune
c p l k h t z d u k e duke
d k d f r u l e x c v rule
e n b c u t e g j h y cute
f m u l e w q s a b m mule
g k t r w s r u d e z rude
h n c u b e p t r w x cube
i k l p y f l u t e c flute
j w q f s z d v u s e use

Test 15

2 hat man cap shin pip
rob hop not tub cut

3 a mane b hope
c tube d shine
e note f pipe
g cute h hate
i robe j cape

Test 16

1 car star bark dark arm
farm card hard start cart

2 a dark b hard
c start

3 a bark b car
c arm d star
e farm f cart
g card

Test 17

1 fast last plaster glass grass
bath path ask mask basket

2 a fast b last c grass
d basket e glass f bath
g path h plaster i mask
j ask

Test 18

1 mouse house mouth south
loud cloud sound found out
shout

2 **out**: out shout
outh: mouth south
ouse: mouse house
oud: loud cloud
ound: sound found

3 a I found a mouse in the house.
b I opened my mouth to shout out loud.
c There was a big black cloud in the south.
d When I am quiet I don't make a sound.

Test 19

1 cow how owl howl growl
flower shower clown down
crowd

2 a cow how owl
b howl down
c growl clown crowd
d flower shower

3 a cow b growl c crowd
d flower e clown

Test 20

1 toy boy joy coy enjoy
employ annoy destroy oyster
royal

2 a oyster
b toy boy joy coy enjoy employ annoy destroy
c royal

3 a boy coy enjoy joy toy
b annoy destroy employ oyster royal

Test 21

1 oil boil coil foil spoil coin join point noise voice

2 boil coil foil spoil

3 a join b coin c point
d voice e noise

Test 22

1 put bush push full pull
book cook look good wood

2 put

3 a push
b pull
c wood
d cook look

4 a Let me look at that cook book.
b It is not nice to pull or push someone in a bush.
c You can't put more water in a glass that is full.
d It is good to walk in the wood.

Test 23

1 head dead bread tread spread heavy ready steady feather weather

2 heavy

3 a dead b bread
c head d spread
e tread f steady
g ready h weather
i feather

Test 24

2 a food boot pool roof broom
b cook wood hook good foot

3 a boot b cook
c foot d wood
e broom f good
g food h roof
i pool j hook

Test 25

2 a beach team seat weak season
b deaf sweat leather jealous meadow

3 a sweat b team
c deaf d season
e seat f beach
g leather h weak
i meadow j jealous

Test 26

1 why what when where which wheel whisk wheat whale white

2 a white b whisk c wheat
d whale e wheel

3 a What is your name?
b Where do you live?
c Why do you go to school?
d When do you go to bed?
e Which fruit do you like best?

Test 27

2 a toothbrush
b playground
c handbag
d rainbow
e moonlight
f seaside
g butterfly
h bookcase
i windmill
j sunshine

3 a rainbow
b seaside
c toothbrush
d playground
e handbag
f butterfly
g bookcase
h sunshine
i windmill
j moonlight

Test 28

2 a January
b February
c March
d April
e May
f June
g July
h August
i September
j October
k November
l December

3 a January
b December
c February
d October
e November

4 April August

Test 29

2 a eye ear lip
b hair nose chin neck face
c cheek
d forehead

3 a lip
b neck
c hair
d face
e nose
f forehead
g eye

4 cheek chin

5 You hear with your ear.

Test 30

2 a mat b table
c door d bath
e sink f clock
g bed h window
i chair j cooker

3 a bath b window
c bed d sink
e clock f chair
g table h door
i cooker j mat

Test 31

2 fog ice

3 wind rain snow mist gale

4 frost sleet

5 sunshine

6 a rain b frost
c gale d mist
e sleet f fog
g snow h ice
i sunshine

Spelling test answers

Test 1

1 ____________________
2 ____________________
3 ____________________
4 ____________________
5 ____________________
6 ____________________
7 ____________________
8 ____________________
9 ____________________
10 ____________________

Score ____

Test 2

1 ____________________
2 ____________________
3 ____________________
4 ____________________
5 ____________________
6 ____________________
7 ____________________
8 ____________________
9 ____________________
10 ____________________

Score ____

Test 3

1 ____________________
2 ____________________
3 ____________________
4 ____________________
5 ____________________
6 ____________________
7 ____________________
8 ____________________
9 ____________________
10 ____________________

Score ____

Test 4

1 ____________________
2 ____________________
3 ____________________
4 ____________________
5 ____________________
6 ____________________
7 ____________________
8 ____________________
9 ____________________
10 ____________________

Score ____

Test 5

1 ____________________
2 ____________________
3 ____________________
4 ____________________
5 ____________________
6 ____________________
7 ____________________
8 ____________________
9 ____________________
10 ____________________

Score ____

Test 6

1 ____________________
2 ____________________
3 ____________________
4 ____________________
5 ____________________
6 ____________________
7 ____________________
8 ____________________
9 ____________________
10 ____________________

Score ____

Test 7

1 ____________________
2 ____________________
3 ____________________
4 ____________________
5 ____________________
6 ____________________
7 ____________________
8 ____________________
9 ____________________
10 ____________________

Score ____

Test 8

1 ____________________
2 ____________________
3 ____________________
4 ____________________
5 ____________________
6 ____________________
7 ____________________
8 ____________________
9 ____________________
10 ____________________

Score ____

Test 9

1 ____________________
2 ____________________
3 ____________________
4 ____________________
5 ____________________
6 ____________________
7 ____________________
8 ____________________
9 ____________________
10 ____________________

Score ____

Test 10

1 ____________________
2 ____________________
3 ____________________
4 ____________________
5 ____________________
6 ____________________
7 ____________________
8 ____________________
9 ____________________
10 ____________________

Score ____

Test 11

1 ____________________
2 ____________________
3 ____________________
4 ____________________
5 ____________________
6 ____________________
7 ____________________
8 ____________________
9 ____________________
10 ____________________

Score ____

Test 12

1 ____________________
2 ____________________
3 ____________________
4 ____________________
5 ____________________
6 ____________________
7 ____________________
8 ____________________
9 ____________________
10 ____________________

Score ____

Test 13

1 ____________________
2 ____________________
3 ____________________
4 ____________________
5 ____________________
6 ____________________
7 ____________________
8 ____________________
9 ____________________
10 ____________________

Score ____

Test 14

1 ____________________
2 ____________________
3 ____________________
4 ____________________
5 ____________________
6 ____________________
7 ____________________
8 ____________________
9 ____________________
10 ____________________

Score ____

Test 15

1 ____________________
2 ____________________
3 ____________________
4 ____________________
5 ____________________
6 ____________________
7 ____________________
8 ____________________
9 ____________________
10 ____________________

Score ____

Test 16

1 ____________________
2 ____________________
3 ____________________
4 ____________________
5 ____________________
6 ____________________
7 ____________________
8 ____________________
9 ____________________
10 ____________________

Score ____

Test 17

1 ____________________
2 ____________________
3 ____________________
4 ____________________
5 ____________________
6 ____________________
7 ____________________
8 ____________________
9 ____________________
10 ____________________

Score ____

Test 18

1 ____________________
2 ____________________
3 ____________________
4 ____________________
5 ____________________
6 ____________________
7 ____________________
8 ____________________
9 ____________________
10 ____________________

Score ____

Test 19

1 ____________________
2 ____________________
3 ____________________
4 ____________________
5 ____________________
6 ____________________
7 ____________________
8 ____________________
9 ____________________
10 ____________________

Score ____

Test 20

1 ____________________
2 ____________________
3 ____________________
4 ____________________
5 ____________________
6 ____________________
7 ____________________
8 ____________________
9 ____________________
10 ____________________

Score ____

Test 21

1 ____________________
2 ____________________
3 ____________________
4 ____________________
5 ____________________
6 ____________________
7 ____________________
8 ____________________
9 ____________________
10 ____________________

Score ____

Test 22

1 ____________________
2 ____________________
3 ____________________
4 ____________________
5 ____________________
6 ____________________
7 ____________________
8 ____________________
9 ____________________
10 ____________________

Score ____

Test 23

1 ____________________
2 ____________________
3 ____________________
4 ____________________
5 ____________________
6 ____________________
7 ____________________
8 ____________________
9 ____________________
10 ____________________

Score ____

Test 24

1 ____________________
2 ____________________
3 ____________________
4 ____________________
5 ____________________
6 ____________________
7 ____________________
8 ____________________
9 ____________________
10 ____________________

Score ____

Test 25

1 ____________________
2 ____________________
3 ____________________
4 ____________________
5 ____________________
6 ____________________
7 ____________________
8 ____________________
9 ____________________
10 ____________________

Score ____

Test 26

1 ____________________
2 ____________________
3 ____________________
4 ____________________
5 ____________________
6 ____________________
7 ____________________
8 ____________________
9 ____________________
10 ____________________

Score ____

Test 27

1 ____________________
2 ____________________
3 ____________________
4 ____________________
5 ____________________
6 ____________________
7 ____________________
8 ____________________
9 ____________________
10 ____________________

Score ____

Test 28

1 ____________________
2 ____________________
3 ____________________
4 ____________________
5 ____________________
6 ____________________
7 ____________________
8 ____________________
9 ____________________
10 ____________________

Score ____

Test 29

1 ____________________
2 ____________________
3 ____________________
4 ____________________
5 ____________________
6 ____________________
7 ____________________
8 ____________________
9 ____________________
10 ____________________

Score ____

Test 30

1 ____________________
2 ____________________
3 ____________________
4 ____________________
5 ____________________
6 ____________________
7 ____________________
8 ____________________
9 ____________________
10 ____________________

Score ____

Test 31

1 ____________________
2 ____________________
3 ____________________
4 ____________________
5 ____________________
6 ____________________
7 ____________________
8 ____________________
9 ____________________
10 ____________________

Score ____